Brazil

ANN CHON

Contents

Chapter 1   Brazil   2

Chapter 2   The Litterbug goes travelling   13

Chapter 3   The Very Important Committee   20

Chapter 4   Bug attack   24

Chapter 5   Home again   30

Chapter 6   A big surprise   39

Chapter 1 Brazil

Professor Quickly was having a fantastic time. He had been to Africa, India, Tibet, Japan and Madagascar and lots of other places. He had collected all sorts of interesting (but safe) animals to bring back to Crack Puzzle House.

He sent them all back to a zoo in Britain where they would be properly looked after until he arrived home.

But Professor Quickly was still very interested in bugs, and there was one more visit he wanted to make. This was to a place where he knew he would be able to study many fantastic bugs and insects. He was flying to the rain forests of Brazil.

Two days later the Professor was sailing up the Amazon River, which led deep into the Brazilian rain forest. This forest stretched for hundreds and hundreds of miles, and many parts of it had still not been explored. Thousands of wonderful trees towered up to the sky, and their green branches and leaves formed a thick roof, blocking out the light. Down on the ground it was dark and murky.

The Professor loved it, and his butterfly net had never had so much use. He spent all day with the net in his hand, gathering insects and bugs of every shape and colour.

He was travelling in a little dug-out boat, and he was so keen on catching insects that he just didn't see the other animals living in the river and trees. Sometimes he stretched so far out over the water that it was a wonder he didn't fall in!

Perhaps if Professor Quickly had known
about some of the animals surrounding him, he
would not have felt so happy. The river
itself was teeming with life, and some of the
animals swimming in the water were quite
horrible!

There were crocodiles. There were little
fish with very sharp teeth that could strip
the flesh from a man in a matter of minutes.

There were little fish that were just as
interested in bugs as the Professor, which came
leaping out of the water to catch any insect
that came flying past. There were wicked-
looking eels that could give a man a nasty
electric shock. There was a turtle with a
funny jagged shell. It lay quite still on
the river bed and snapped up any fish that
swam too close. So it is very lucky that
the Professor did not fall into the water.

And when the Professor landed on the river banks, he was still so interested in catching his bugs that he did not see the other animals living in the forest.

There were animals lurking everywhere. The rain forest is so full of hazards, that it is often called the 'green hell'!

But it was the same here as everywhere else. The animals trusted the Professor and nothing bothered him or attacked him.

Every night, when he set up his camp, and lit a small fire outside his tent, the animals would gather round and watch him.

Hundreds of green and yellow eyes gleamed in the darkness. Some of the braver animals came and sat next to him. Not one of them tried to harm him. And luckily, Professor Quickly did not try to put any of them in his pocket.

But then came the night of the last camp. The Professor was packing up the crates he was going to take back with him. He had set free all the bugs he had collected and the wooden crates were full of plants, seeds and saplings. The Professor was lashing the crates to a boat with thick ropes. The next day a bigger boat was coming to pull it down the river.

While he was doing this, a little family of animals crept up in the darkness and watched him intently. They kept completely still to make quite sure that the Professor could not see them.

Then, as soon as he went back to his tent and snuggled down into his sleeping bag for a good night's sleep, the little animals began to move.

The next day the Professor began the long
trip down the Amazon River. But he did not
know that some little animals had hitched a
lift with him!

Chapter 2   The Litterbug goes travelling

On the day before Professor Quickly arrived home, the Litterbug was sitting in the greenery just outside his cave feeling fed up and bored stiff. He had loved teasing the Professor, but the Professor had been away for months and the house was empty and quiet. The Litterbug hated quiet. He had nothing to do.

It was no fun messing things up just for the sake of it – it was only fun if someone was upset at the end of it – and now there was no-one to upset.

Every six years or so the Litterbug got fed up like this. When that happened he went off by himself. He travelled for miles and miles and visited different towns up and down Britain.

'Time to push off again,' he muttered to himself. 'It's about time I had some proper fun!'

14

After travelling for three miles, the Litterbug came to a crossroads.

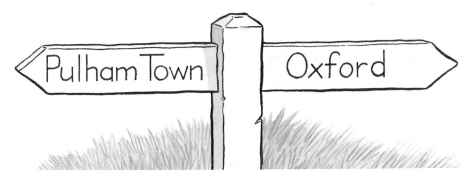

'Pulham Town!' chuckled the Litterbug. He thought it was a very funny name.

'Hee-hee! I'll pull them down in Pulham Town.' And he set off again. As he came to the outskirts of Pulham, this is what he saw:

The Litterbug found this even funnier.

'Hee, hee,' he chuckled. 'This is getting better and better. I'll make sure that they never win another prize again.'

He knew that the first thing he must do was to find a safe base. He needed to find somewhere to hide. He kept going, passing neat houses and gardens, well-kept parks and brightly painted shops. Before long he arrived in the middle of the town. Now the shops were much bigger. There were supermarkets, do-it-yourself shops, big bookshops, banks, snack bars, shops selling carpets and beds and wallpaper and sports goods and lots more.

The Litterbug knew it was no good looking for somewhere to hide in the main street. He knew that the backs of big shops are nowhere near as neat and clean as the front. He crept down a side street, and sure enough, he was right. The Litterbug's eyes lit up. The street behind the shops was a mess. There were piles of boxes, bins crammed so full of rubbish that their lids wouldn't fit on properly, black sacks with rips and gashes in them so the filth inside them came tumbling out, and bits of litter everywhere.

A black cat prowled in and out of the rubbish, though it was difficult to tell if it was looking for scraps to eat or if it was hunting for rats.

'They all make life so easy for me!' whispered the Litterbug to himself. 'If they got rid of their rubbish every day I wouldn't have so much stuff to fling around.'

The Litterbug loved mess, but even he did not intend to spend the rest of the night in the rubbish he had just seen. He had to find somewhere else.

He kept on going and at last he came to the back of the do-it-yourself shop. There was a big rubbish skip parked at the back of this shop. The Litterbug knew that do-it-yourself stores do not have to get rid of bits of rotting food, which attracts rats and other vermin. This was just the place he was looking for. He could hide here for the rest of the night, and then he could get on with the thing he did best, which was to turn this town into a shambles.

Chapter 3 The Very Important Committee

At ten o'clock the next morning the Litterbug woke up, climbed out of the skip and moved into the main street. No-one saw him because he moved so fast.

What the Litterbug didn't know was that today was a very important day for the town. The day of 'The Best Kept Town Contest', which was held once a year, had come round again.

A Committee of Very Important Persons was just setting out to inspect the town. They were coming down the steps of the Town Hall. The Committee would look at all the main parts of the town and give marks for neatness and cleanness. Last year the town had got full marks (the Committee did not look down the back streets!) and Pulham had got first prize as the Best Kept Town.

Everyone hoped that they would win first prize again this year, but they were all in for a big disappointment.

The Litterbug didn't know about the Very Important Committee, and it wouldn't have mattered if he did. All he wanted to do was to get on with the job.

He planned to go to the bottom of the
street and work his way upwards. He reached
the bottom just five minutes before the Very
Important Committee reached the top.

Chapter 4 Bug attack

The Litterbug started with the Supermarket. It was full of shoppers, but that made things better. The Litterbug loved to see shoppers jump and scatter when he got going.

He went to the drinks department first.

CRASH! BASH! CLATTER!

Bottles of lemonade, tonic water, wine, rum, vodka, and brandy went flying.

Before the last bottle hit the ground, the Litterbug arrived at the tinned food department. Stacks of cans went crashing down.

The same thing happened in the other departments. The shoppers couldn't understand it. Mums began to smack their children and tell them to keep their hands still.

'Now look what you've done!' they shouted.

The confused children didn't know what to do. So they just sat down and wailed!

The Litterbug was back outside now. He dashed in and out of the shops as fast as the wind.

The shoppers in the Do-it-Yourself shop had to duck and hide as showers of nails came down like rain. Tins of paint came flying past, and splattered everyone in different colours. Brushes, wallpaper, bottles of turpentine, trowels, hammers, drills, and garden tools all hit the ground. A hosepipe flashed past like a thin, green snake – in fact one of the girls thought it was a snake and she fainted.

The assistant in the Sports Shop couldn't understand it. All the neat racks of sports goods ended up in a tangled heap. Ten different sorts of ball went flying down the main street, tripping shoppers up and making even more mess.

When the Litterbug had finished with the shops he started with the street. All the litter baskets went crashing over, their rubbish spilling onto the pavement.

Just at that moment the Very Important Committee came round the corner. So far, their trip round town had been splendid. It looked like Pulham Town was going to win first prize again. But it didn't look that way for very much longer! The Committee were just in time to meet a set of filthy dustbins which came tumbling and spinning out of a side street. There was no time to get out of the way. The Committee went down like skittles! And while they lay on the ground, wondering what had hit them, the Litterbug bombarded them with hanging baskets.

Then the Litterbug saw a blue flashing light and heard the sound of a siren,

EE–AR! EE–AR! EE–AR!

'Time to go!' he panted. 'This is fun! I think that I'll visit some more towns now!'

If he'd only known that on this very day Professor Quickly had come home, the Litterbug would have gone rushing back to Crack Puzzle House, and the Professor's problems would have started much sooner!

29

Chapter 5 Home again

Just as the Litterbug was running away from Pulham Town, Professor Quickly was pulling up outside Crack Puzzle House. The Hardwicks were there to meet him. They helped him to unload the crates and stack them up, then the Professor unlocked the front door.

There was a big pile of letters on the mat, and many of them looked like bills! But the Professor pushed them to one side, and before long everyone was sitting in the kitchen as the Professor told them all about his adventures in far-off lands. The Professor's tales were so interesting that the time passed very fast, and Polly saw that Tom and Kate had fallen asleep.

'Goodness me, look at the time!' she said. 'It's ten past eleven! We should all be in bed.'

The Professor suddenly remembered the crates were still outside.

'We'll get them in the morning,' he said with a yawn. 'Let's all go to bed.'

Later that night there was a sudden movement in one of the crates which were stacked on the drive. And then, just as the moon came out from behind a cloud, ten little animals squeezed out into the open.

They were odd-looking little things. They had big round heads, two arms and two legs, bright eyes and mouths that always seemed to smile.

They stretched out, for they had been cooped up in the crate for several weeks. Then they began to jump up and down and trot on the spot. They were feeling cold which is no surprise as they were used to the hot jungles of Brazil!

They looked around, and were pleased to see that they were in a very big garden.

'Good,' said one, 'there is plenty of work for us to do here!'

These animals were called 'gleeks' and their job in life was to look after living things. The gleeks huddled together and began to chatter. Their first job was to find a safe place to live. They scuttled across the drive and hid underneath the nearest bush. Then a scouting party was sent out to inspect the garden and look for a base.

The scouting party did a good job, and it did not take them long to find the maze with a bubbling fountain in the very middle. This was an ideal spot. It was a safe place and it had a water supply. They reported back to the others, and everyone quickly agreed that the maze would become their base.

Soon, there was a little line of creatures scurrying across the lawn in the moonlight.

They made their way to the middle of the
maze, then they settled down for the night.
At dawn the next day they woke up and
started work. The first job they had to do was
to build their home. Gleeks are very timid, and
they do not like anyone to see them, so they
live deep underground in well-made tunnels.

The gleeks looked at the stone slabs at the base of the fountain. They could see that it would be easy to use one of those slabs as a hidden doorway.

Before long there was a pile of dirt by the side of the fountain. But the gleeks did not let it stay there for anyone to see, they took it away and sprinkled it onto the flower beds in the garden.

The gleeks were very fast workers, but it took five long days of digging to finish their home. By the fifth day they had made a network of tunnels which stretched far beyond the maze, and led to every part of the garden. Every so often, they had put in a hidden exit, so that any gleeks that were disturbed while they were out in the garden could quickly vanish.

Each tunnel led back to the gleeks' den. This was a wonderful place. It was divided up into several different rooms with little doors made out of woven twigs and rushes.

They had made little wooden beds with fresh hay and straw to sleep on, and their seats were made from the living tree roots.

Each room had a small shaft leading up to the ground, to let in the sunlight and cool breezes. At the top of each shaft was a clever trapdoor, which the gleeks could close whenever they wanted.

Now that their den was finished, they were ready to start exploring the garden.

Chapter 6 A big surprise

While the gleeks were hard at work, the Professor was sorting out all the things that had piled up over the year he had been away.

He was not a happy man. There were a lot of bills to pay, and the Professor had spent too much on his trip.

Each envelope he opened seemed to contain an even bigger bill. He piled up all the bills in front of him.

Now there were just two envelopes left. He opened one. It was another bill, this time from the zoo that was looking after all the animals he had sent back. He knew he couldn't pay it. The Professor sat and thought.

If he couldn't pay the bill, he couldn't get the animals back.

If he couldn't get the animals back he couldn't open his park.

If he couldn't open his park he couldn't sell tickets to the public.

If he couldn't sell tickets, he would never have enough to pay his bills!

It was a difficult problem, and he didn't think that he could find an answer. Perhaps he'd have to let the zoo keep all his animals, sell Crack Puzzle House, move back into a flat and find another job.

He looked at the last envelope. He didn't want to open it. He couldn't stand to look at another bill. But he knew he must. Very slowly he slit open the envelope and pulled out the white sheet of paper from inside.

He read it. Then he read it again. Then he jumped out of his seat and shouted,

'Yippee!'

He'd just been left thousands of pounds!